SCALE DRAWINGS
PLANS AND BEARINGS

ANSWERS

PETER ROBSON

 **Newby Books**

PO Box 40, Scarborough
North Yorkshire YO12 5TW
Tel/Fax 01723 362713
www.newbybooks.co.uk

The answers in this book are given to an accuracy that could be expected from a student drawing and measuring with basic school equipment. Answers of a greater accuracy can, in many cases, be obtained by calculation, trigonometry, etc.

On pages 24 to 38 (questions 82 to 122) an arrow pointing to the top of the page indicates North.

© Peter Robson 2010

ISBN 978-1-872686-36-3

Printed by G. H. Smith & Son, Easingwold, York YO61 3AB
Telephone 01347 821329. Facsimile 01347 822576
www.ghsmith.com

1. (a) 11 000 mm   (b) 2 650 mm   (c) 1 000 mm   (d) 2 200 mm   (e) 600 mm   (f) 16 mm
(g) 114 mm   (h) 25 mm   (i) 47 mm   (j) 14 mm

2. (a) 600 cm   (b) 32 000 m   (c) 1 740 cm   (d) 800 000   (e) 39 m   (f) 5.4 km   (g) 18.70 m
(h) 33.5 cm   (i) 620 000 cm   (j) 49.800 m

3. (a) 1:100   (b) 1:8 000   (c) 1:350   (d) 1:500 000   (e) 1:200   (f) 1:3 000   (g) 20:1
(h) 1:375 000   (i) 1:1 000 000   (j) 1:50 000

4. 105 m

5. (a) 15 m   (b) 10 cm   (c) 7.8 m   (d) 43 cm   (e) 1.5 m

6. (a) 15 cm   (b) 7 cm   (c) 105 cm^2

7. (a) 2 mm   (b) 32.5 mm   (c) 100 mm   (d) 9 mm   (e) 75 mm

8. (a), (b)

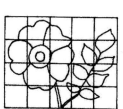

9. (a) 10.8 m   (b) 4.3 m   (c) 15.8 m   (d) 2.2 m   (e) 4.7 m

10. (a) 16 m   (b) 7.5 m   (c) 2 m   (d) 5 m   (e) 11 m   (f) 9 m   (g) 4.5 m^2 (h) 1.5m^2 (i) 90°
(j) 70°   (k) 3.5 m   (l) 8.5 m   (m) 6.25 m^2 (6^1/$_4$ m^2)   (n) 1.25 m^2 (1^1/$_4$ m^2)   (o) 135°

3

11.

Map Length	Actual Length
1 cm	2.5 km
3 cm	**7.5 km**
12 cm	30 km
5 cm	12.5 km
1.6 cm	**4 km**
22 cm	**55 km**

12. (a) 2 200 m   (b) 300 m   (c) 1 400 m   (d) 500 m   (e) 200 m   (f) 60 m

13. (a) 1:3 ($^1/_3$)   (b) 2:1 (2)   (c) 1:1 000 ($^1/_{1\,000}$)   (d) 1:32 ($^1/_{32}$)   (e) 1:50 ($^1/_{50}$)

14. (a) 25 mm   (b) 15 mm   (c) 9 mm   (d) 7 mm   (e) 4 mm

15.

Scale	Length	Width
1:100	4 cm	3 cm
1:50	8 cm	6 cm
1:200	2 cm	1.5 cm
1:10	40 cm	30 cm
1:25	16 cm	12 cm
1:20	20 cm	15 cm

16. (a) 64 m   (b) 60 m   (c) 20 m

17. (a) 10 m   (b) 20 m   (c) 35 m   (d) 7.5 m   (e) 50 m

18. (a) 1:2 000   (b) 80 m   (c) 260 m   (d) 10 cm^2 *or* 1 000 mm^2 (e) 4000 m^2

19. (a) 1 km   (b) 4 km   (c) 3.5 km   (d) 1.5 km   (e) 6 km

20. (a) 900 m   (b) 375 m   (c) 600 m   (d) 750 m   (e) 975 m
   Scale factor 1 cm : 150 m *or* 1:15 000

21. (a) 200 m   (b) 150 m   (c) 400 m   (d) 125 m   (e) 225 m   (f) 775 m   (g) 650 m   (h) 550 m
   (i) Trenton Way, Anderby Road and Craig Lane   (j) 22 500 m^2

22. (a) 1:130   (b) 18.2 m

23. (a) 2 km   (b) 17 km   (c) 4 cm   (d) 11.5 cm   (e) 1:200 000

24. (a) 1.5 m   (b) 4.5 m   (c) 12 m   (d) 6 m   (e) 15 m

25. (a) 145 miles   (b) 75 miles   (c) 95 or 100 miles   (d) 105 or 110 miles   (e) 455 or 460 miles
   (f) 295 miles   (g) 40 miles   (h) 160 or 165 miles   (i) 465 or 470 miles   (j) 255 or 260 miles

26. (a) 1:150   (b) rectangle   (c) trapezium   (d) 6.0 m   (e) 3.0 m   (f) 4.5 m   (g) 2.25 m ($2^1/_4$ m)
   (h) 9 m^2 (i) 13.5 m^2 (j) 11.25 m^2 ($11^1/_4$ m^2)

27. (a) 600 m   (b) 250 m   (c) 500 m   (d) 250 m   (e) 650 m   (f) 700 m   (g) 500 m   (h) West
    (i) South   (j) East

28. Scale 1:50

(a)

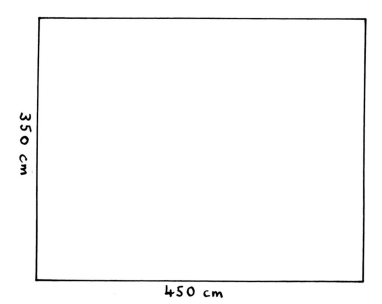

(b) 63 cm²

29. (a) 400 m   (b) 200 m   (c) 400 m   (d) 160 m   (e) 320 m   (f) 240 m   (g) 120 m   (h) 360 m
    (i) 480 m   (j) 520 m

30. (a) Scale 1 mm to 1 m (1:1000)

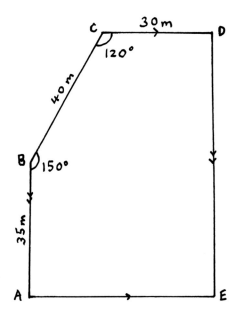

(b) 50 m

31. (a) Scale 1 cm to 1 m (1:100)

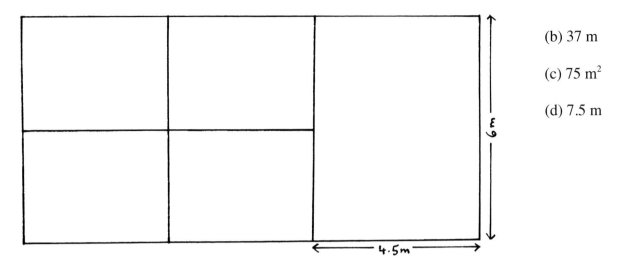

(b) 37 m

(c) 75 m^2

(d) 7.5 m

32. (a) Scale 1 cm to 5 m (1:500)   (b) 300 m^2 (c) 1 000 m^2

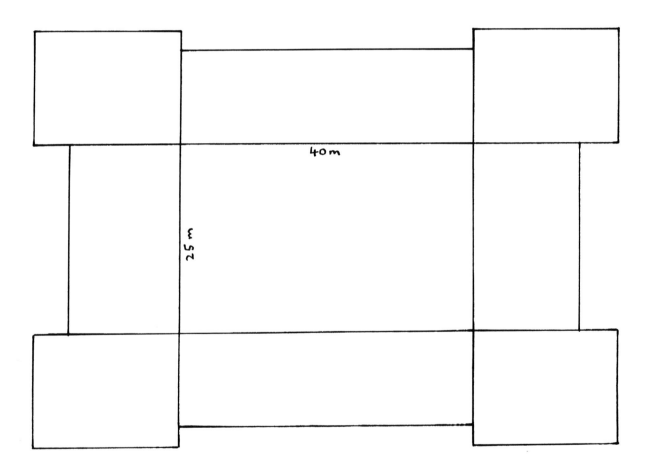

33. Scale 1 cm to 25 km (1:2 500 000)

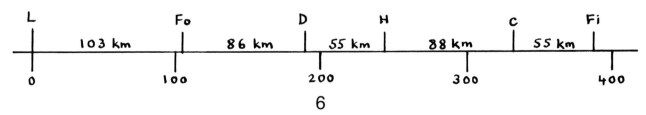

6

34. Scale 1 cm to 50 miles

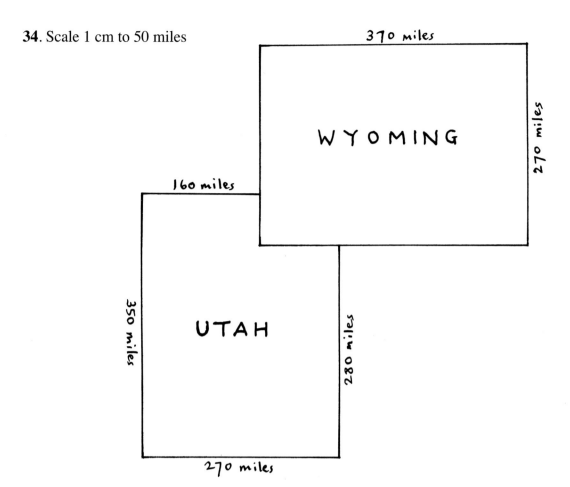

35. (a) Scale 1 cm to 40 m (1:4000)

(b) 390 m

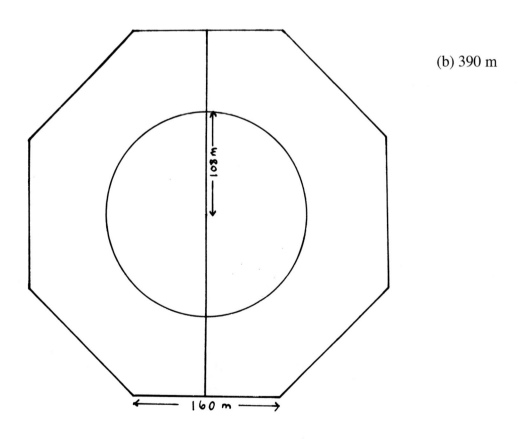

36. (a)

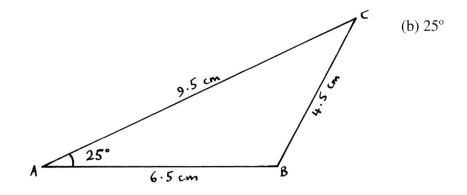

(b) 25°

37. (a)

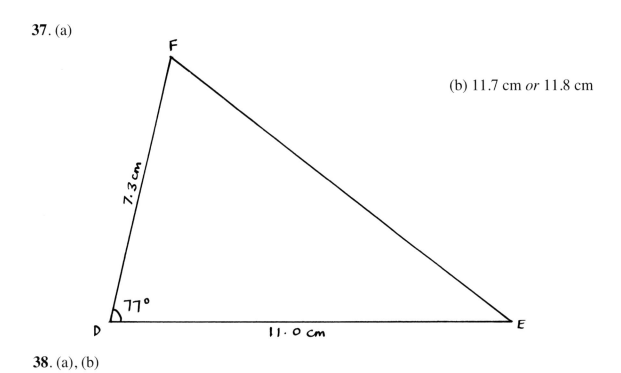

(b) 11.7 cm *or* 11.8 cm

38. (a), (b)

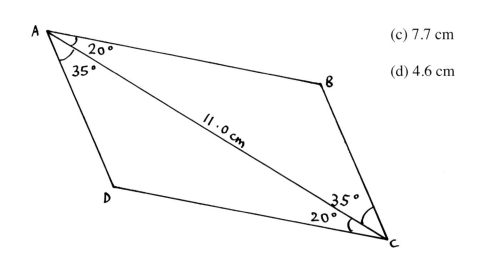

(c) 7.7 cm

(d) 4.6 cm

39. (a), (b), (c)

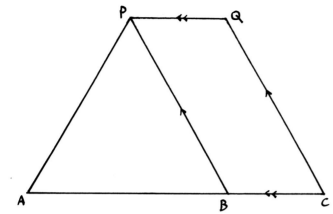

(d) parallelogram
(e) trapezium (isosceles trapezium)

40. (a), (b), (c), (d), (e)

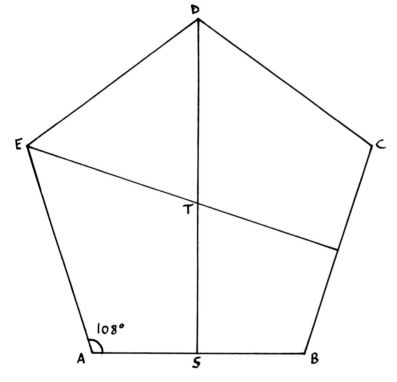

(f) 40 mm

(g) regular pentagon

41. (a), (b), (c), (d)

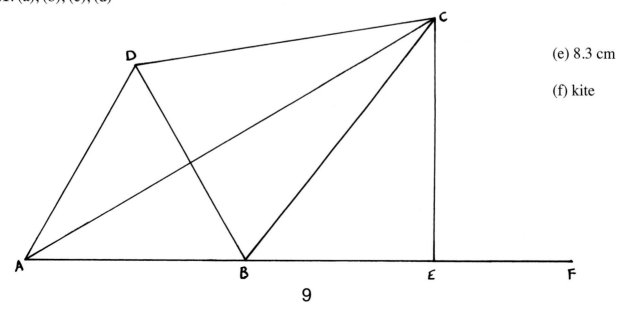

(e) 8.3 cm

(f) kite

42. (a), (b)

(c) 66°

(d) 8.1 cm

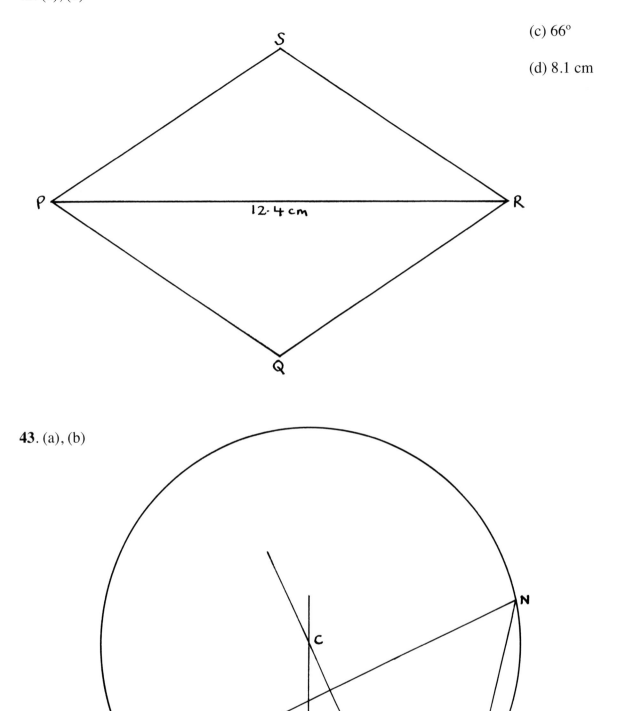

43. (a), (b)

(c) If the measurements have been accurate, the circumference passes through points L, M and N

44. (a), (b), (c)

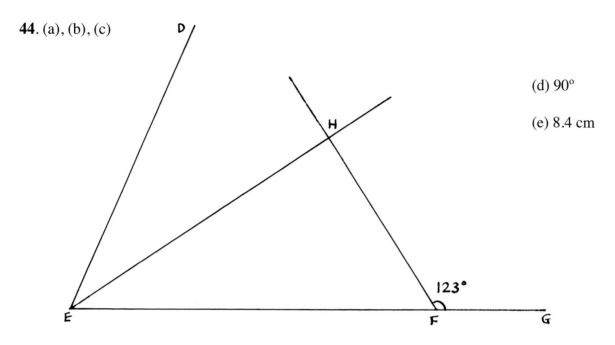

(d) 90°

(e) 8.4 cm

45. (a), (b)

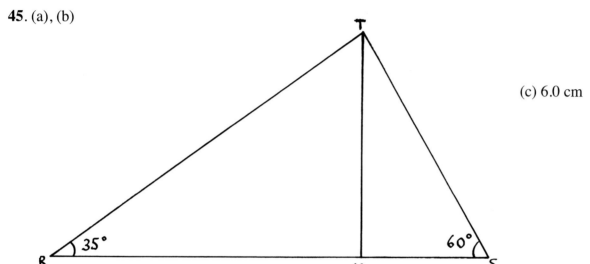

(c) 6.0 cm

46. (a), (b)

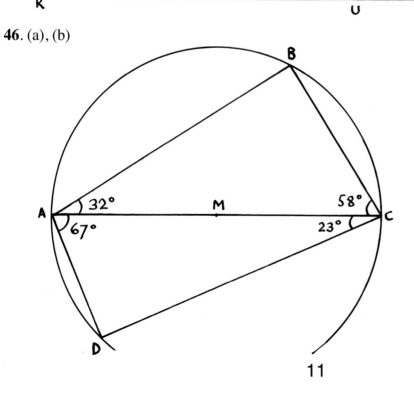

(c) If the measurements have been accurate, points A, B, C and D all lie on the circumference of the circle.

(d) isosceles

(e) 116°

11

47. (a)

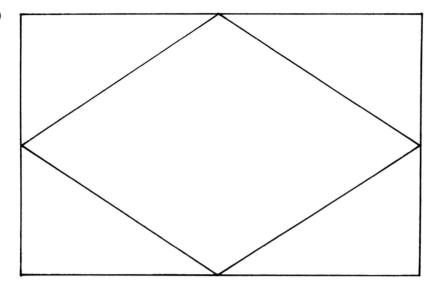

(b) rhombus

(c) 115°

(d) ¹/₂

48. (a), (b)   Scale 1 cm to 40 m (1:4 000)

(c) 240 m

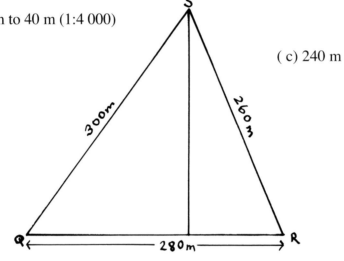

49. (a), (b)

(c) ¹/₂₄

If the pattern is repeated, the result is 17 whole squares and 14 half squares, making a total of 24 squares.

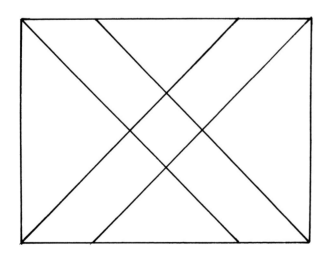

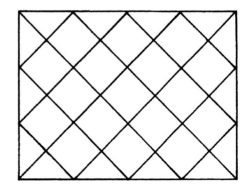

12

50. Scale 1 cm to 100 m (1:10 000)

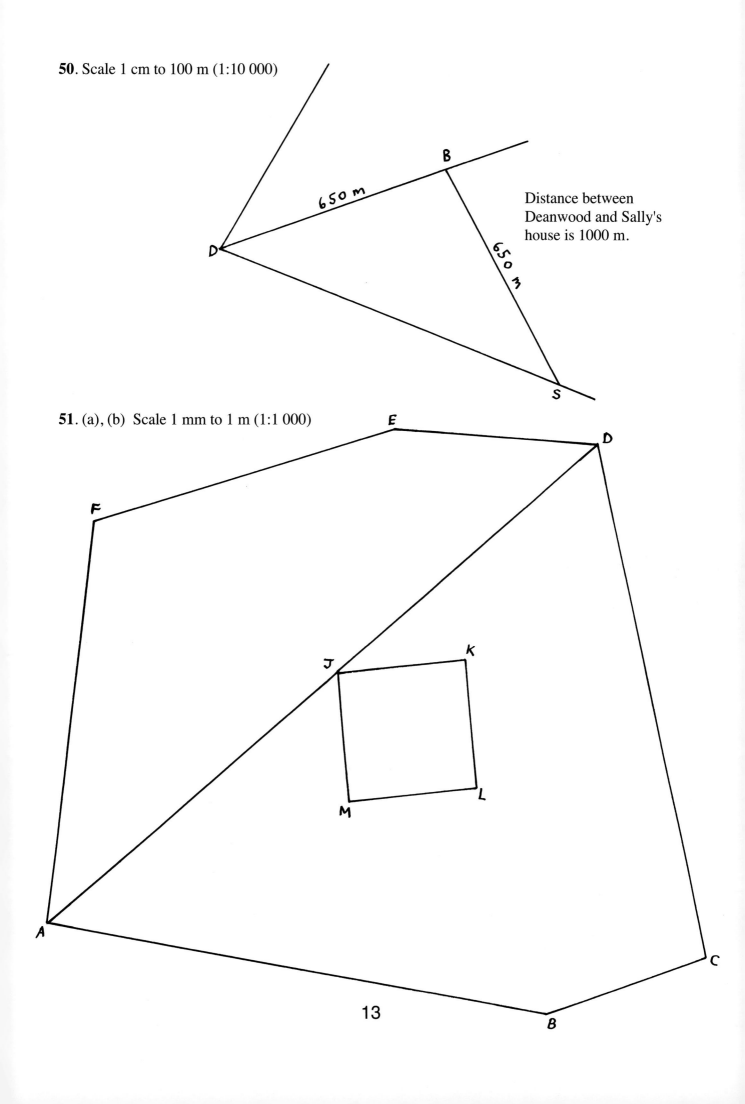

650 m

650 m

Distance between
Deanwood and Sally's
house is 1000 m.

51. (a), (b) Scale 1 mm to 1 m (1:1 000)

13

52. Scale 1 cm to 1 m (1:100)

(a)

(b) 100°

[**53**. See opposite page (page 15)]

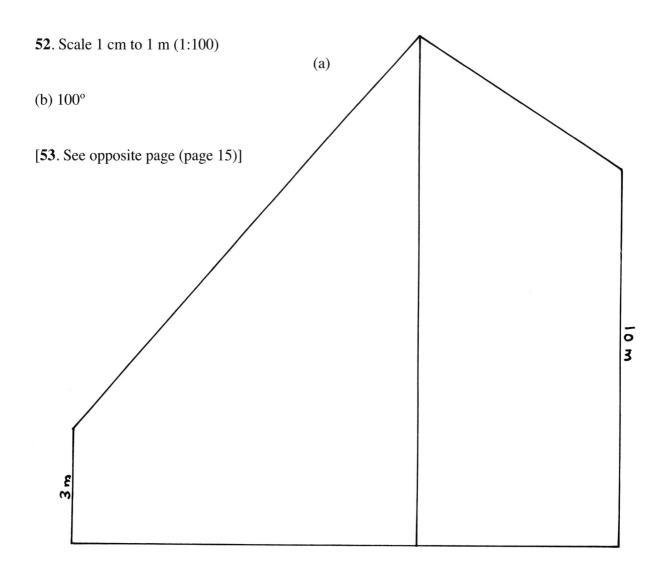

10 m

3 m

54. (a), (b), (c), (d)

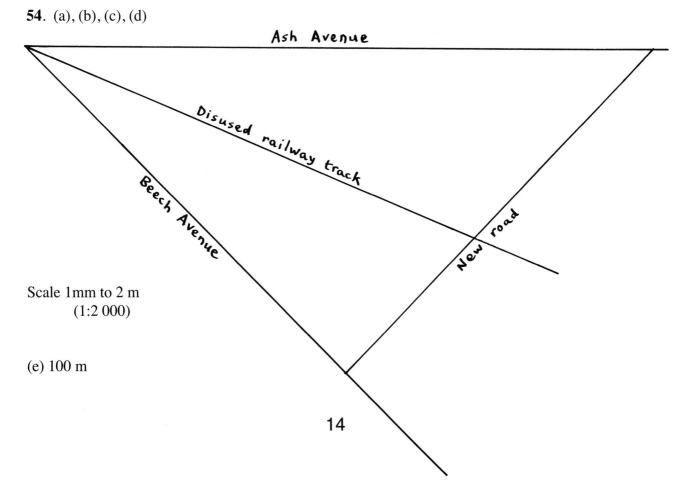

Ash Avenue

Disused railway track

Beech Avenue

New road

Scale 1mm to 2 m
(1:2 000)

(e) 100 m

53. (a), (b), (c), (d), (e), (f)

(g) 1: 100 000 000

(h) 6900 km

(i) 1900 km

(j) North

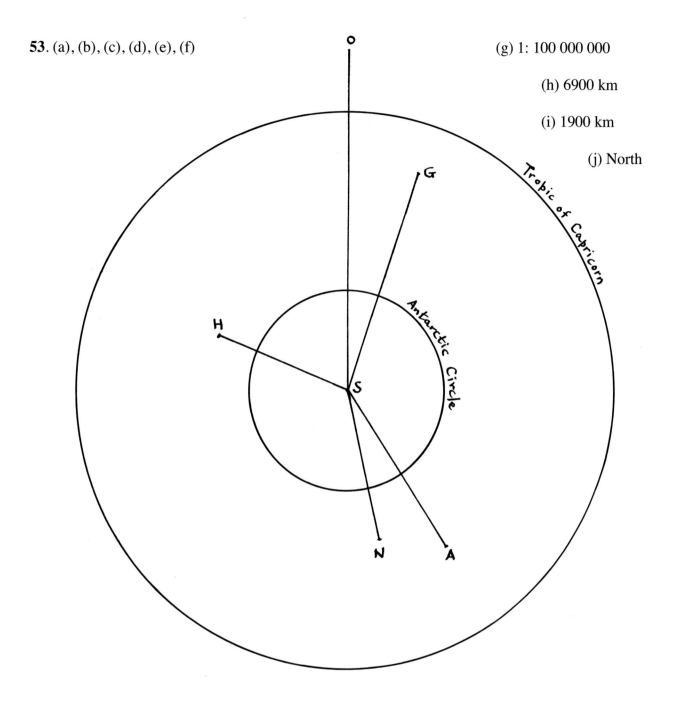

[**54.** See opposite page (page 14)]

55.

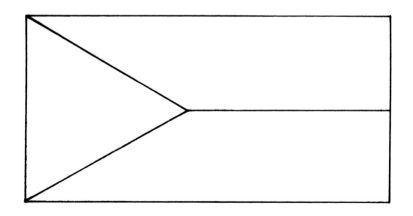

56.

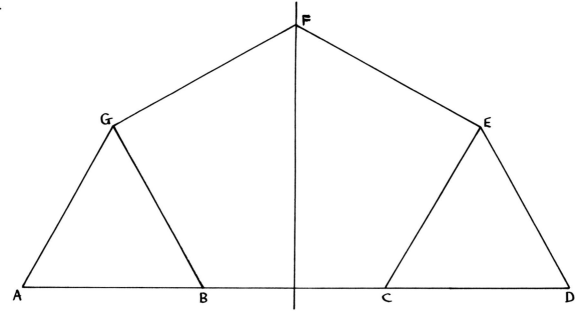

57. (a), (b), (c), (d)

(e) North Pole and
      South Pole

(f) Equator

(g) Upper line represents
      the Tropic of
      Cancer; lower
      line represents
      the Tropic of
      Capricorn.

(h) Right-hand side
      (NLCAQS)
      represents line of
      longitude 0°;
      left-hand side
      (STEN)
      represents line of
      longitude 180°.

(i) 2000 km

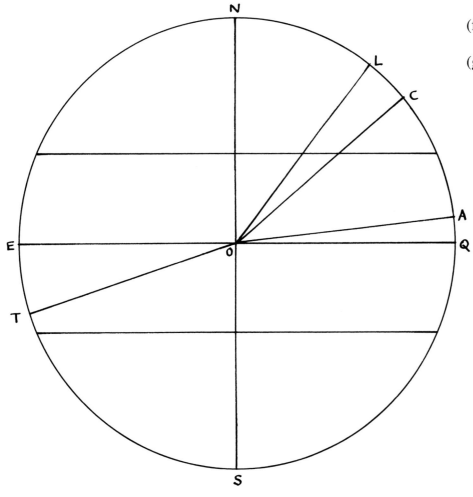

58. Scale 3mm to 1 m

Height of tower is 23 m.

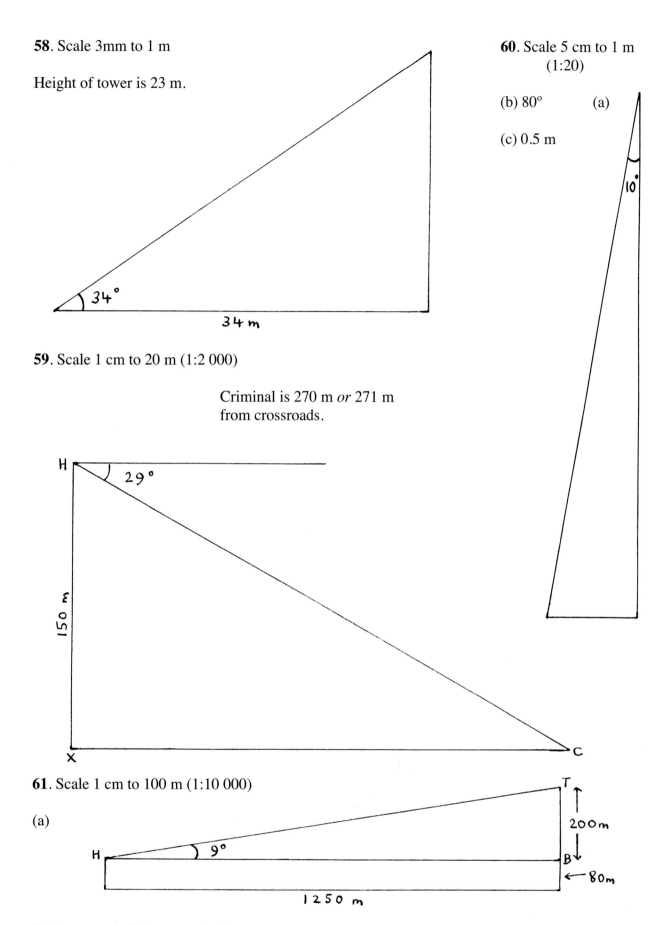

34°

34 m

60. Scale 5 cm to 1 m
(1:20)

(b) 80°   (a)

(c) 0.5 m

10°

59. Scale 1 cm to 20 m (1:2 000)

Criminal is 270 m *or* 271 m
from crossroads.

H 29°

150 m

X   C

61. Scale 1 cm to 100 m (1:10 000)

(a)

H 9°

1250 m

T

200m

B

←80m

(b) Bottom of cliff to top of cliff is 200 m.
Cliff top is 200 + 80 = 280 m above sea level.

62. Scale 1 cm to 20 m (1:2 000)

(a)

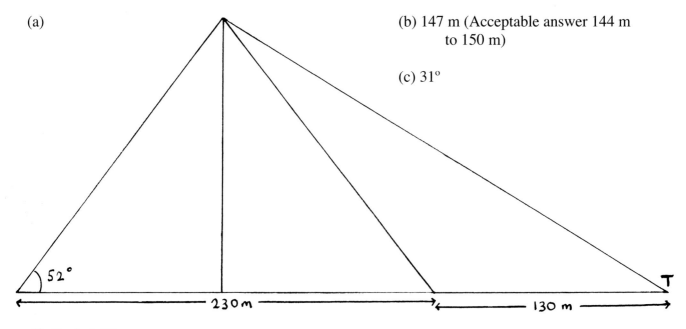

(b) 147 m (Acceptable answer 144 m to 150 m)

(c) 31°

63. Scale 1:30

(a)

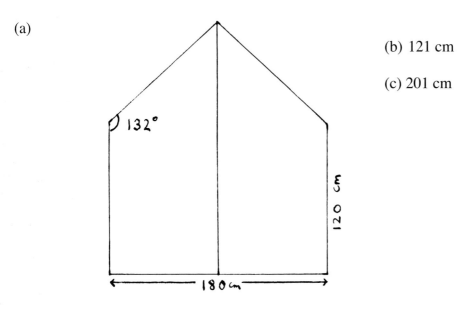

(b) 121 cm

(c) 201 cm

64.   Scale 1 cm to 50 m (1:5 000)

(a)

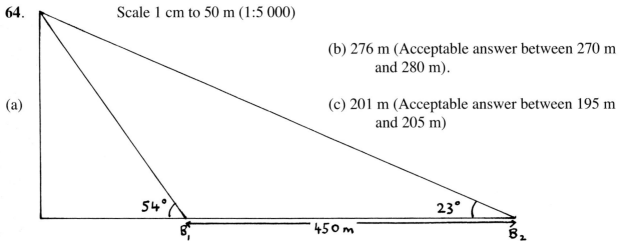

(b) 276 m (Acceptable answer between 270 m and 280 m).

(c) 201 m (Acceptable answer between 195 m and 205 m)

18

65. Scale 1 cm to 1 m (1:100)

(a)

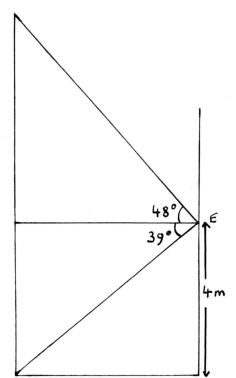

(b) 5 m

(c) 9.5 m

66. Scale 1 cm to 10 m (1:1 000)

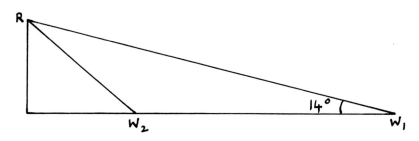

(a) 25 m

(b) 70 m

67. Scale 1mm to 10 m (1:10 000)

(a)

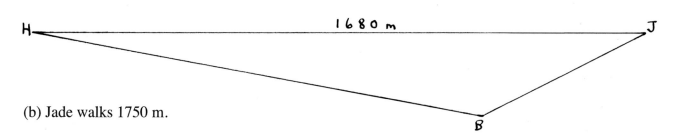

(b) Jade walks 1750 m.

68. Scale 1 cm to 1 m (1:100)

(a)

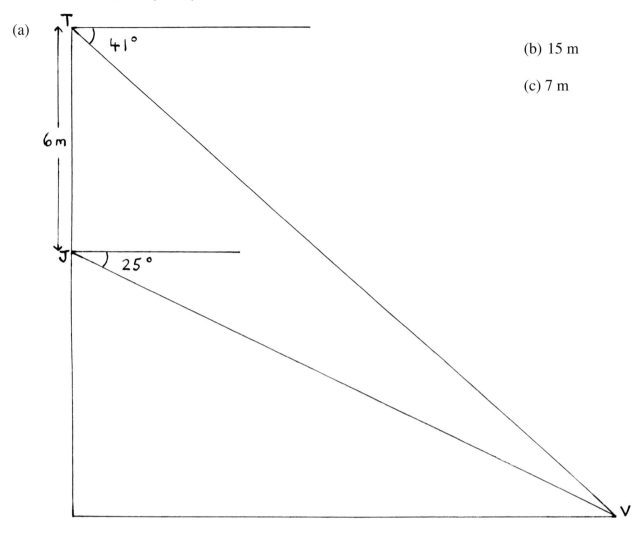

(b) 15 m

(c) 7 m

69. (a) 300 m   (b) 700 m   (c) About 9°   (d) About 2500 m   (e) About 5 cm

70. Scale 1 cm to 2 m (1:200)

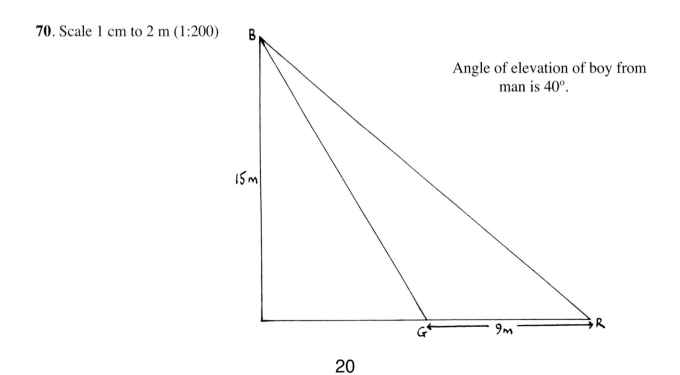

Angle of elevation of boy from man is 40°.

71. Scale 1 cm to 10 m (1:1 000)

(a) 21°

(b) 14°

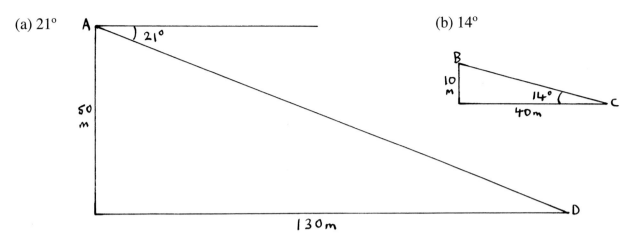

(c) 45°

(d) 20°   (e) Dot and Eddie

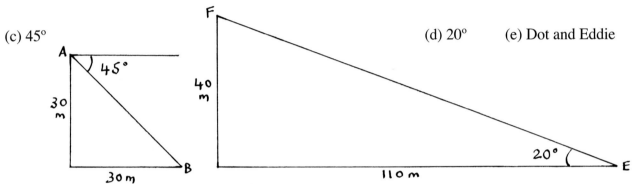

72. Scale 1 cm to 10 m (1:1 000)

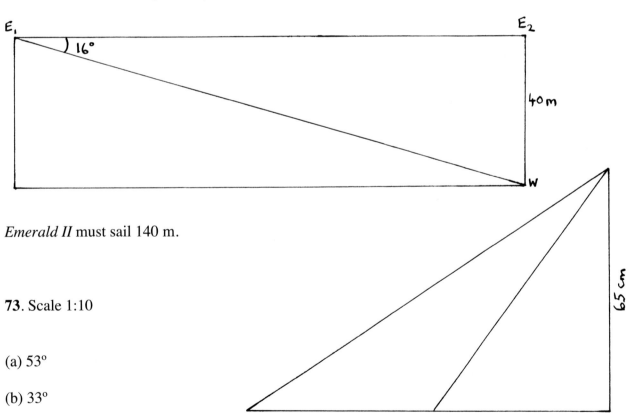

Emerald II must sail 140 m.

73. Scale 1:10

(a) 53°

(b) 33°

74. Scale 2 cm to 1 km (1:50 000)

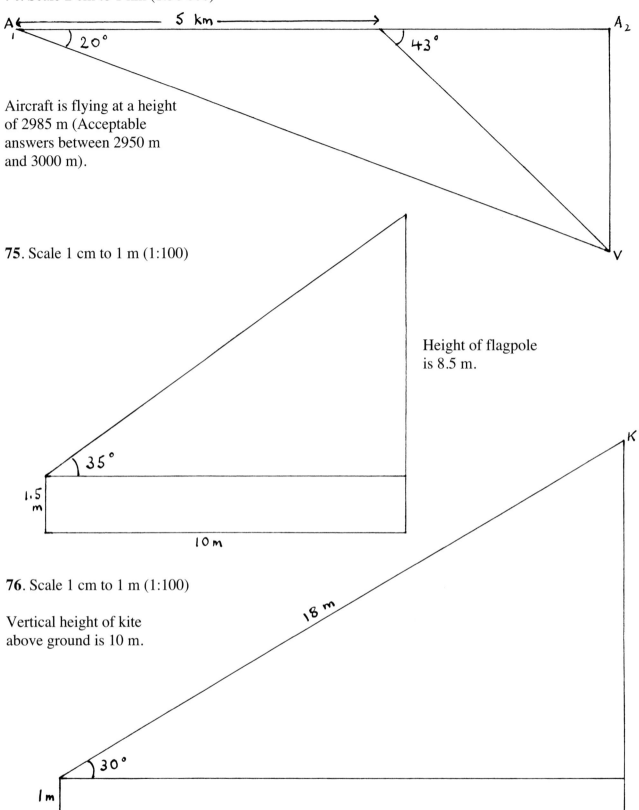

Aircraft is flying at a height
of 2985 m (Acceptable
answers between 2950 m
and 3000 m).

75. Scale 1 cm to 1 m (1:100)

Height of flagpole
is 8.5 m.

76. Scale 1 cm to 1 m (1:100)

Vertical height of kite
above ground is 10 m.

77. (a) E   (b) SW   (c) NW   (d) N   (e) SE

78. (a) 45°   (b) 90°   (c) 135°   (d) 45°   (e) 180°

79. Scale 1 cm to 1 m (1:100)

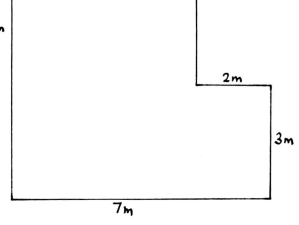

(a) 5 m

(b) East

80. Scale 1 cm to 2 m (1:200)

(a) 24 m

(b) North East (NE)

81. 1 cm to 4 m (1:400 000)

(a) 8 km

(b) West

23

82. Scale 1 cm to 1 km (1:100 000)

(a) Approximately SE
(b) 8.4 km or 8.5 km

83. (a) 45° (b) 90° (c) 135° (d) 90° (e) 135°

84. (a) 270° (b) 020° (c) 294° (d) 001° (e) 146° (f) 317° (g) 085° (h) 238° (i) 172° (j) 039°

85. (a) 225° (b) 000° (c) 135° (d) 315° (e) 180°

86. (a) 130° (b) 068° (c) 232° (d) 337° (e) 084° (f) 011° (g) 116° (h) 299° *or* 300° (i) 215°
(j) 180°

87. (a) 50 mm (b) 68 mm (c) 100 mm (d) 065° (e) 245° (f) 038° (g) 218° (h) 000° (i)180°

88. (a) 045° (b) 225° (c) 331° (d) 151° (e) 283° (f) 104° (g) 7.8 cm (h) 8.9 cm (i) 15.6 m
(j) 20.0 m

24

89. Scale 1 cm to 1 km (1:100 000)

(a) 260°
(b) 206°
(c) 049°
(d) 229°
(e) 12.5 km

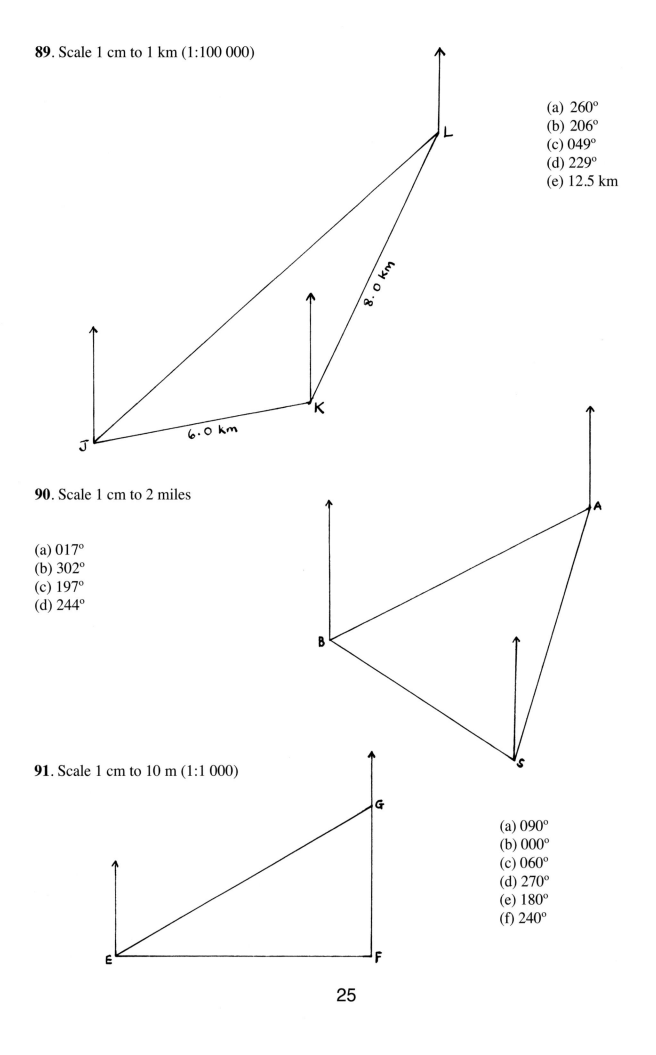

90. Scale 1 cm to 2 miles

(a) 017°
(b) 302°
(c) 197°
(d) 244°

91. Scale 1 cm to 10 m (1:1 000)

(a) 090°
(b) 000°
(c) 060°
(d) 270°
(e) 180°
(f) 240°

92. Scale 1 cm to 1 km (1:100 000)

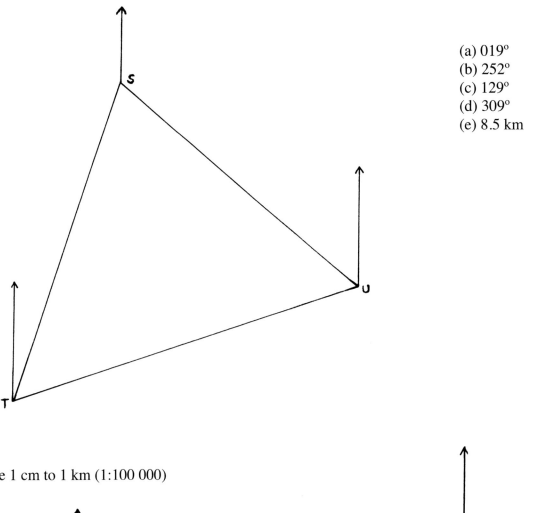

(a) 019°
(b) 252°
(c) 129°
(d) 309°
(e) 8.5 km

93. Scale 1 cm to 1 km (1:100 000)

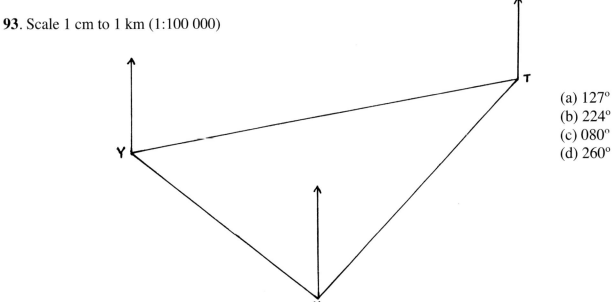

(a) 127°
(b) 224°
(c) 080°
(d) 260°

94. (a) 13 km   (b) 18 km   (c) 24 km   (d) 17 km   (e) 231°   (f) 300°   (g) 052°   (h) 157°

(i) 72 km   (j) 092°

95. Scale 1 mm to 1 m (1:1000)

(a) 225°
(b) 067°
(c) 121 m

96. 1 cm to 200 m (1:20 000)

(a) 328°
(b) 2.8 km

97. 1 cm to 2 km (1:200 000)

(a) 038°
(b) 218°

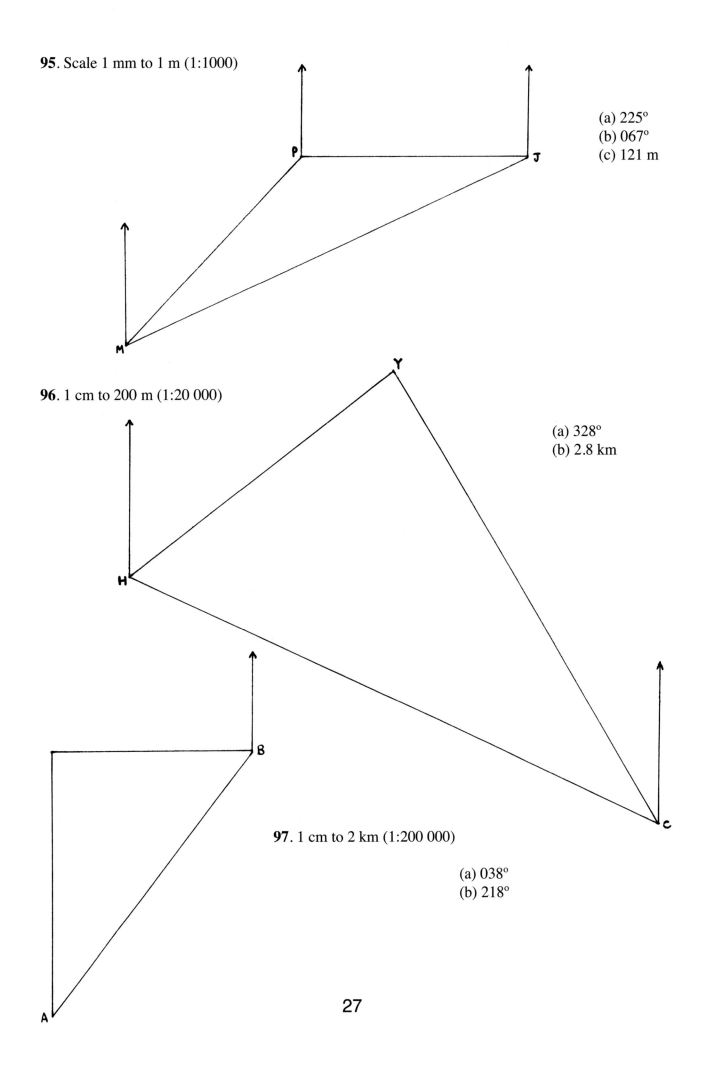

27

98. Scale 1 cm to 100 m (1:10 000)

(a) 1960 m
(b) 1000 m
(c) 198°

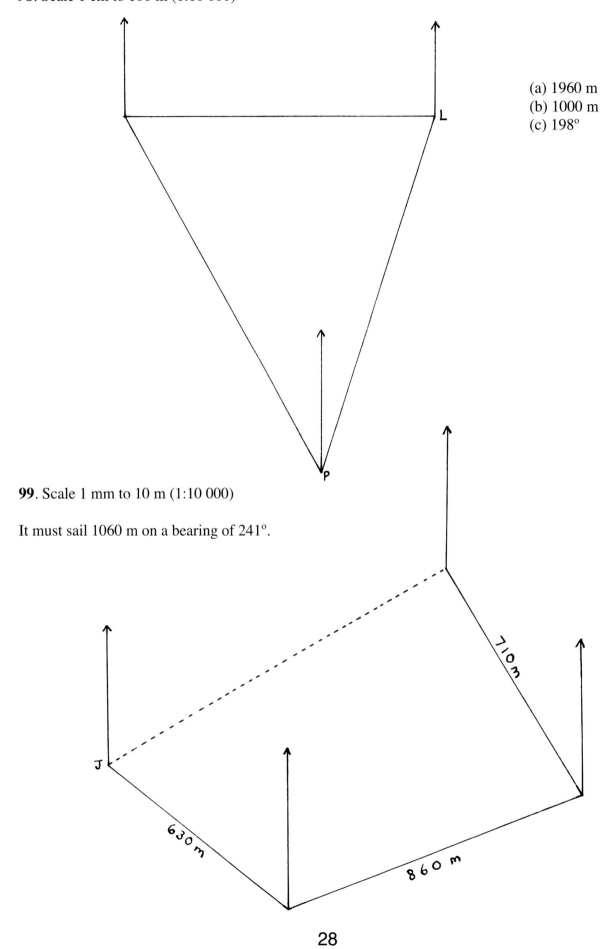

99. Scale 1 mm to 10 m (1:10 000)

It must sail 1060 m on a bearing of 241°.

100. Scale 1 cm to 1 mile

P   A

(a) 090°
(b) 10.5 miles

101. Scale 1 cm to 40 m (1:4 000)

                                                    G

(a) 400 m
(b) 300 m
(c) 240 m
(d) 270°

                    B

                                                    S

102. Scale 1 cm to 10 km (1:1 000 000)

(a) 57 km
(b) 89 km
(c) SW
(d) 40 km
   or 41 km

103. Scale 1 cm to 2 miles

(a) 19 miles
(b) 032°

104. Scale 1 cm to 1 km (1:100 000)

(a) 153°
(b) 240°
(c) 294°
(d) 333°
(e) 9 km

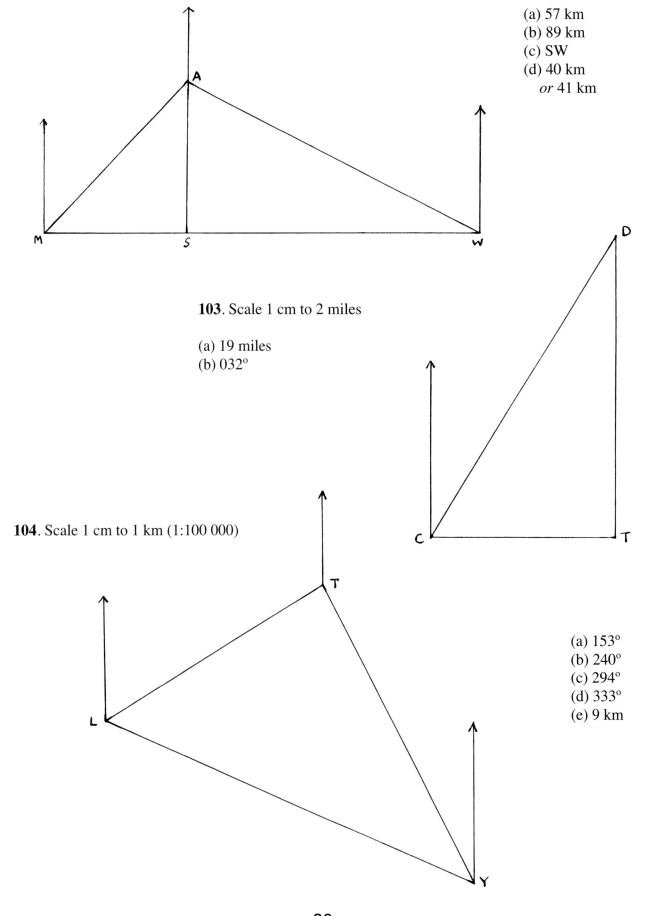

105. (a) 342° (b) 044° (c) 1 000 m (d) About 800 m (e) About 1 200 m

106. Scale 1 cm to 1 km (1:100 000)

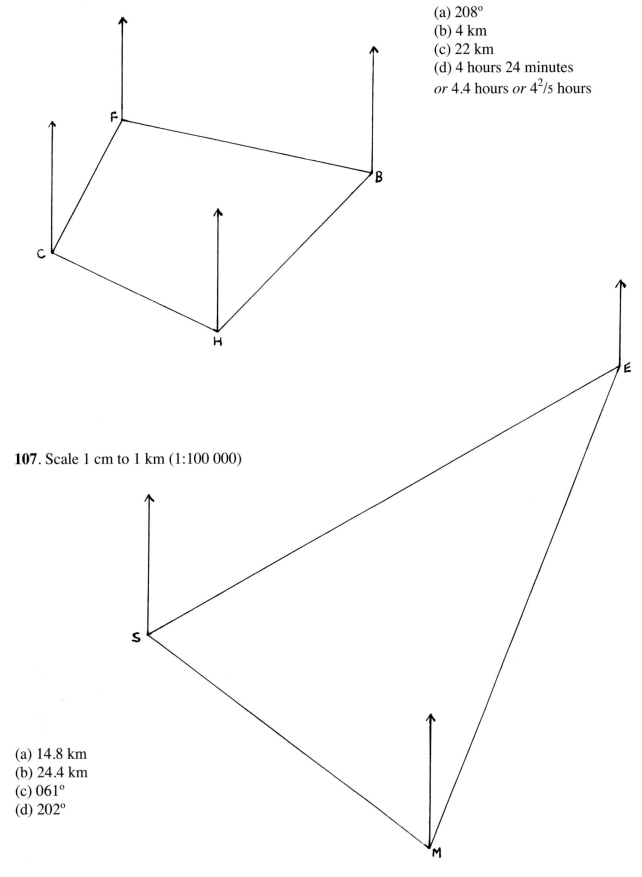

(a) 208°
(b) 4 km
(c) 22 km
(d) 4 hours 24 minutes
or 4.4 hours *or* $4^2/5$ hours

107. Scale 1 cm to 1 km (1:100 000)

(a) 14.8 km
(b) 24.4 km
(c) 061°
(d) 202°

108. (a) 064° (b) 139° *or* 140° (c) 16.9 km (d) 2.7 km *and* 10.2 km (e) 15.5 km (f) 13.4 km (g) 287° (h) 4.9 km *or* 5.0 km

109. Scale 1 cm to 50 m (1:5 000)

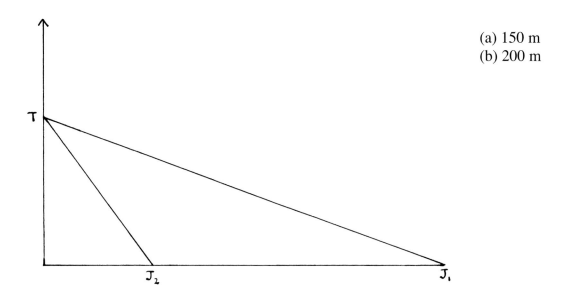

(a) 150 m
(b) 200 m

110. Scale 1 cm to 1 km (1:100 000)

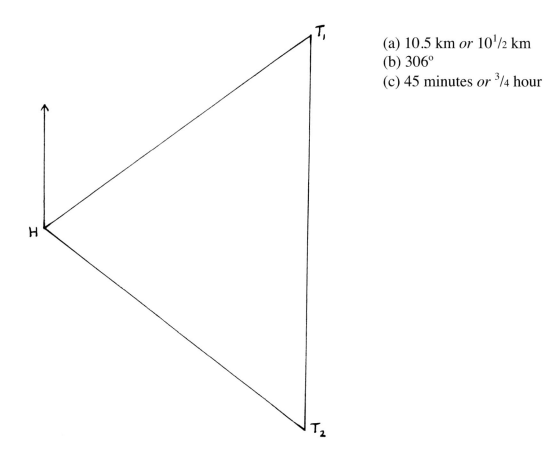

(a) 10.5 km *or* $10\frac{1}{2}$ km
(b) 306°
(c) 45 minutes *or* $^3/_4$ hour

111. Scale 1cm to 1 km (1:100 000)

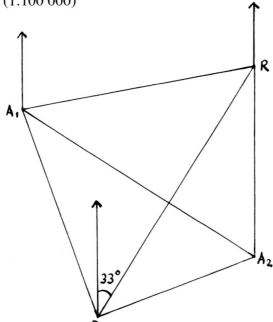

(a) 122° *or* 123°
(b) 7.5 km
(c) 225 km/h

112. Scale 2 cm to 1 km (1:50 000)

(a) 279° *or* 280°
(b) 4.5 km

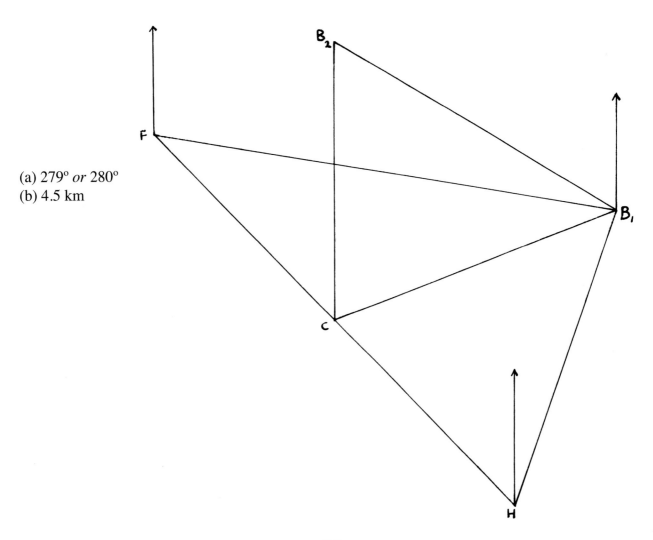

33

113. Scale 1 cm to 1 km (1:100 000)

(a) 12.5 km
(b) 136°
(c) 4.5 km

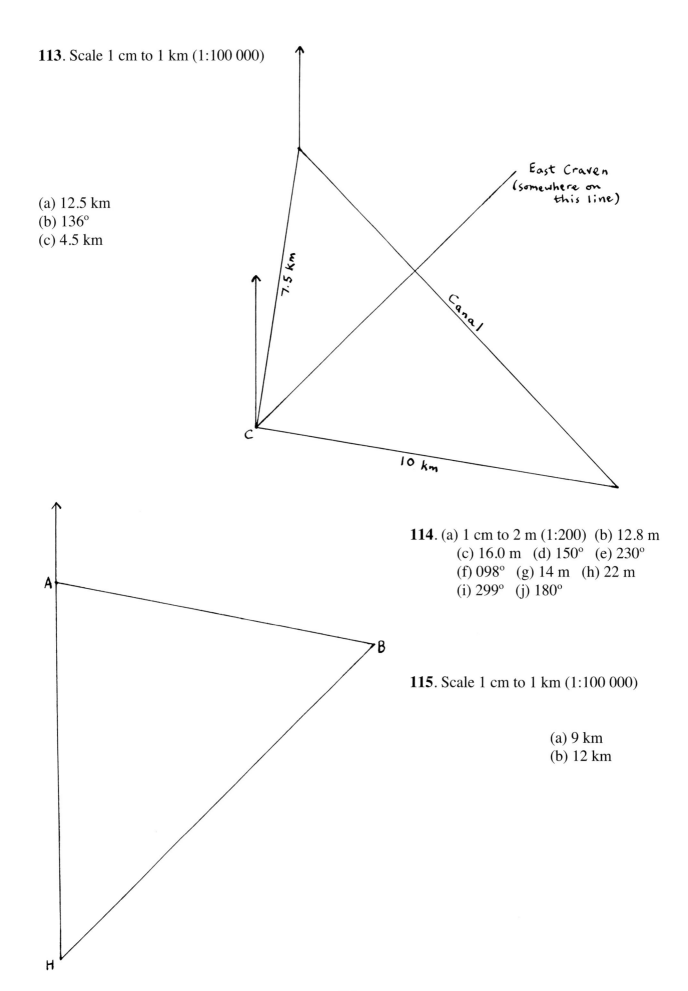

East Craven
(somewhere on
this line)

7.5 km

Canal

C

10 km

114. (a) 1 cm to 2 m (1:200) (b) 12.8 m
(c) 16.0 m (d) 150° (e) 230°
(f) 098° (g) 14 m (h) 22 m
(i) 299° (j) 180°

115. Scale 1 cm to 1 km (1:100 000)

(a) 9 km
(b) 12 km

A

B

H

116. Scale 1 cm to 1 mile

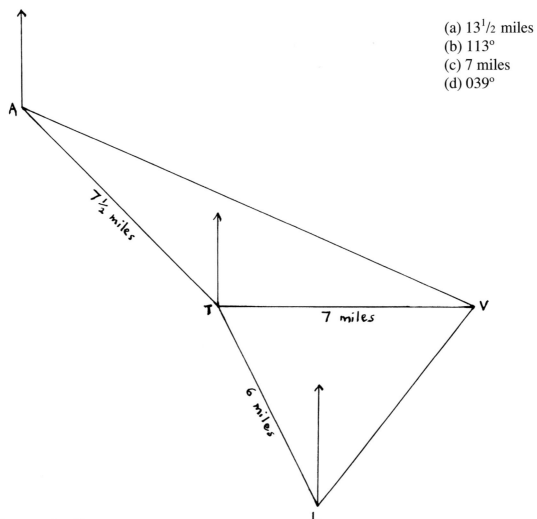

(a) $13\frac{1}{2}$ miles
(b) 113°
(c) 7 miles
(d) 039°

117. Scale 1 cm to 1 mile

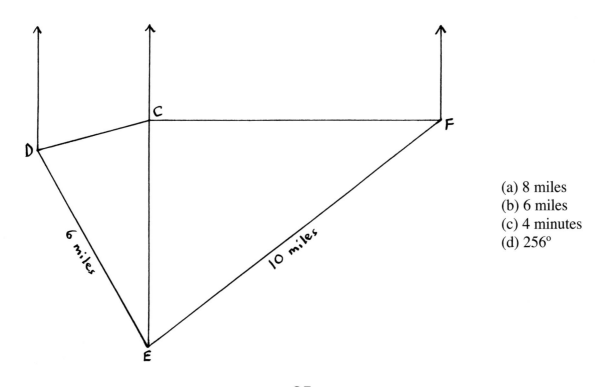

(a) 8 miles
(b) 6 miles
(c) 4 minutes
(d) 256°

118. Scale 1 cm to 20 m (1:2 000)

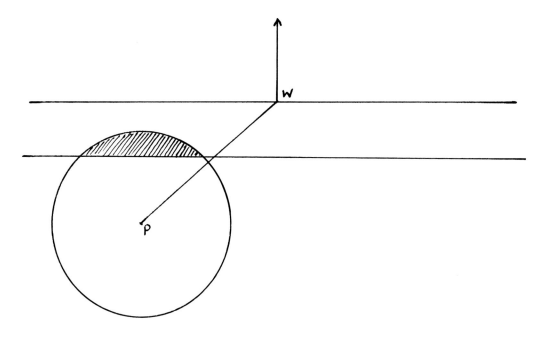

119. (a) Scale 1 cm to 200 m (1:20 000)

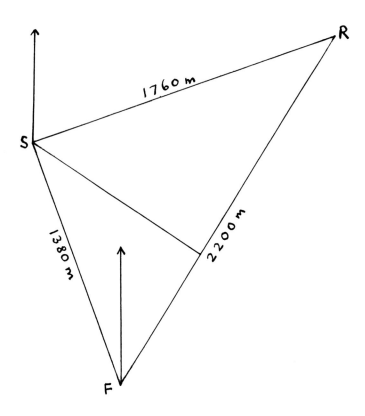

(a) The position of Shardley Hall can be found by drawing arcs with centres at Fenbury and Redlington.

(b) 339°
(c) 071°
(d) 1100 m

120. Scale 1 cm to 5 km (1:500 000)

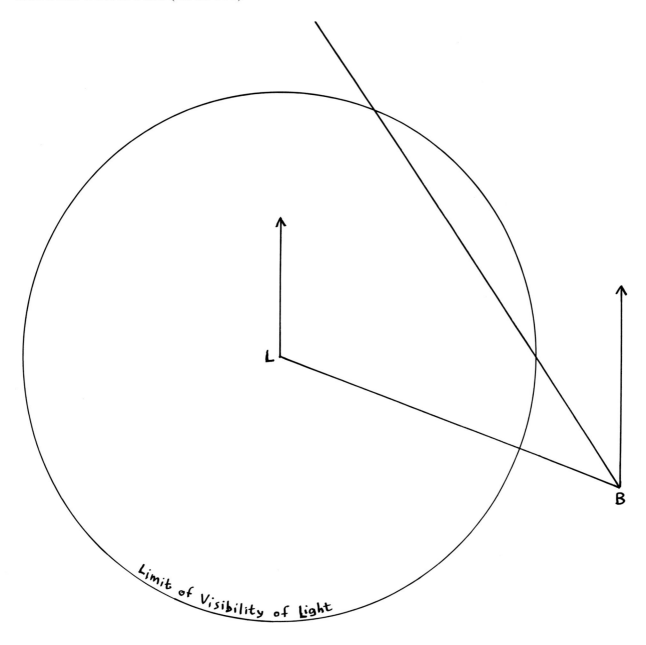

Limit of Visibility of Light

The Saltrock light will be visible for approximately 40 km of the journey.

121. Scale 1 cm to 1 km (1:100 000)

(a) 13.4 km
(b) 9.0 km

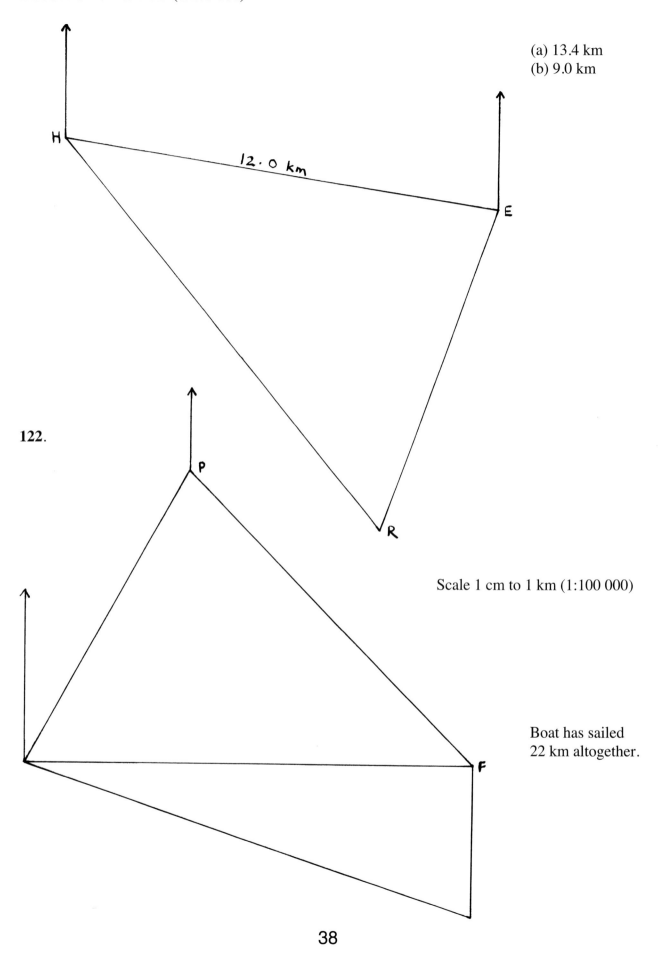

H

12.0 km

E

R

122.

P

Scale 1 cm to 1 km (1:100 000)

Boat has sailed
22 km altogether.

F

123. Scale 1 cm to 1 mile

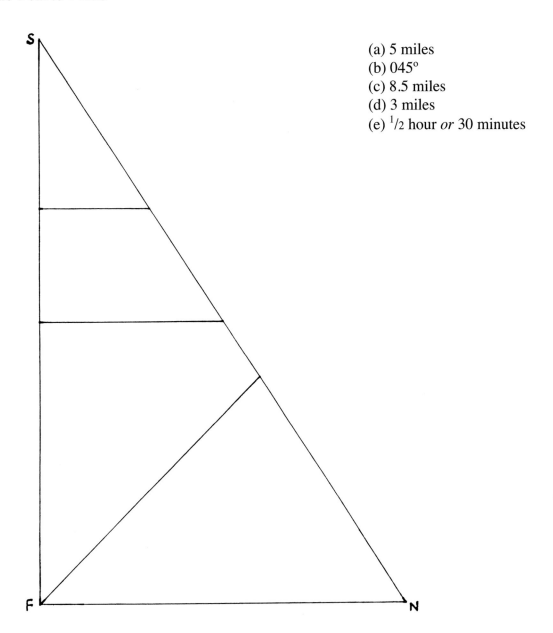

(a) 5 miles
(b) 045°
(c) 8.5 miles
(d) 3 miles
(e) $^1/_2$ hour *or* 30 minutes

124. (a) Birmingham   (b) Newcastle upon Tyne   (c) Dover   (d) Liverpool   (e) Wick

125. (a) 100 km   (b) 800 km   (c) 700 km   (d) 350 km   (e) 500 km

126. (a) Orkney Islands   (b) Isle of Man   (c) Cornwall   (d) TQ   (e) ST   (f) SH   (g) NT
(h) English Channel   (i) NS   (j) SM   (k) Scilly Isles   (l) HP   (m) Severn   (n) SZ
(o) North West Highlands

127. (a) Derby   (b) Gainsborough   (c) Melton Mowbray   (d) Lichfield   (e) Sheffield
(f) Lincoln   (g) Buxton   (h) Leicester   (i) Mansfield   (j) Grantham

128. A: SK 1040   B: SK 6075   C: SK 2520   D: SK 9555   E: SK 5050

129. (a) 105 km   (b) 146°   (c) 320°   (d) 63 km *or* 64 km   (e) 40 miles

130. (a) Hulland   (b) Mugginton   (c) Osmaston Park   (d) Biggin   (e) Bradley Oldpark
  (f) Turnditch   (g) Brailsford   (h) Atlow   (i) Blackbrook Farm   (j) Corley Farm

131. (a) 7.9 km   (b) 057°   (c) SK 215495   (d) SK 270440   (e) SK 225450

132. (a) 958283   (b) 006284   (c) 981269   (d) 005315   (e) 019240   (f) IH 962317
  (g) IH 997242   (h) IJ 025313   (j) IJ 013306   (j) IH 960265

133. (a) 1 km   (b) 6.9 km   (c) 3.5 km   (d) 2 km   (e) 8.5 km

134. (a) N   (b) SW and NE   (c) SE   (d) W   (e) SW   (f) 130°   (g) 340°   (h) 087°   (i) 221°
  (j) 015°

135. (a) 1 km^2 (b) 80 km^2 (c) 500 m   (d) 70 m   (e) 8°

136. (a) 82°N   (b) 34°S   (c) 45°N   (d) 19°S   (e) 39°N   (f) 34°S   (g) 64°S   (h) 90°S   (i) 25°N
  (j) 64°N   (k) Blackhorn Klint   (l) Buenos Aires   (m) James Ross Island and Vilyuysk

137. (e) 160°E   (b) 28°W   (c) 90°W   (d) 177°E   (e) 103°E   (f) 14°W   (g) 140°E   (h) 117°W
  (i) 35°E   (j) 99°W

138. (a) 129°W   (b) 42°E   (c) 0°   (d) 147°E   (e) 175°W

139. (a) 150°W   (b) 58°W   (c) 106°E   (d) 67°E   (e) 99°W   (f) 38°E   (g) 158°E   (h) 26°W
  (i) 122°W   (j) 140°E   (k) Georgetown and Palikir   (l) Anchorage

140. (a) 1700   (b) 1500   (c) 0700   (d) 2200   (e) 0800   (f) 1200   (g) 0200   (h) 1800   (i) 11
  (j) seven o'clock in the morning (0700)

141. (a) Thursday   (b) Sunday   (c) Monday   (d) Wednesday   (e) March 16   (f) July 31
  (g) Tuvalu

142. (a) 27°20'   (b) 100°48'   (c) 59°06'   (d) 84°50'   (e) 147°24'   (f) 123°35'   (g) 98°09'
  (h) 68°40'   (i) 77°12'   (j) 12°45'